Text copyright © Coral Rumble 1999
Illustrations copyright © Joanna Higgins 1999

First published in Great Britain in 1999
by Macdonald Young Books
an imprint of Wayland Publishers Ltd
61 Western Road
Hove
East Sussex
BN3 1JD

Find Macdonald Young Books on the internet at
http://www.myb.co.uk

The right of Coral Rumble to be identified as the author
and Joanna Higgins the illustrator of this Work has been
asserted by them in accordance with the
Copyright, Designs and Patents Act 1988

The following poems were first published as follows:
A Goldfish Writes a Poem About His Experiences, Come Here, Miss Eva Garibaldi, When My Dad Watches the News, You're Dead: Babboons' Bottoms (Initiative Press, 1995).
Reasonable Parents, Sorry: A Feast of Good Stories (Lion, 1997).
There's a Frog Down the Back of the Toilet, Miss, Parents' Evening: Excuses, Excuses (O.U.P., 1997).
Lost Property: Unzip Your Lips (Macmillan, 1998).
Patterning: Animal Poems (Scholastic, 1998).
Little Lies: Poems About Me (Wayland, 1998).
Subtraction: Teacher's Pets (Macmillan, 1999).
My Aunt: Verse Forms (Folens, 1999).

Designed by Don Martin
Printed and bound by Guernsey Press

British Library Cataloguing in Publication Data available

ISBN: 0 7500 2826 2

Creatures, Teachers and Family Features

CORAL RUMBLE

Illustrated by Joanna Higgins

MACDONALD YOUNG BOOKS

Contents

Introduction

For me, poetry is the fascinating challenge of word juggling – and once you've learnt one trick you just can't wait to try some more. The poet's job is to choose words carefully and then 'throw' them with skilful precision, so that the magic of rhythm and good timing keeps them all in the right place!

Of course, the poet's job also involves observation – noticing things. There are poems lurking everywhere around us. The poet must hunt them down and capture them on the page. Taste, look, listen, touch, sniff the air and say to yourself, "There's a poem around here somewhere!" – then swoop down with your pen and write it!

Coral Rumble

CREATURES
(The creepy, the cruel and the crazy)

Dry Dog

Dry dog
On a log,
Sees a puddle
In the middle
Of a field.

Dry dog
Jumps from log,
Tiptoes by,
Nose to sky,
Sniffing hard.

Dry dog
Steps in bog,
Paws sink down,
Doggy frown,
Splash, whine, panic!

Dry dog
Slides in bog,
Eyeballs frog,
Soggy dog...
Back on log.

A Goldfish Writes a Poem About his Experiences

I am a goldfish.
I have a seven-second memory,
Or so they say.

I am a goldfish.
I have a seven-second memory,
Or so they say.

I am a goldfish.
I have a seven-second memory,
Or so they say.

I am a goldfish.
I have a seven-second memory,
Or so they say.

I am a goldfish.
I have a seven-second memory,
Or so they say.

I am a goldfish.
I have a seven-second memory,
Or so they say.

I am a goldfish.
I have a seven-second memory,
Or so they say.

I am a goldfish.
I have a seven-second memory,
Or so they say.

I am a goldfish.
I have a seven-second memory,
Or so they say.

I am a g—

Beetle Lout

Weevil snout
Sticking out
Elephantine
Beetle lout.

There's no yield
In any field
That can produce
A weevil shield.

Swots

In your local library,
After closing time,
Undiscovered visitors
Always stay behind.

If you listen carefully
You'll hear the pages turning
As countless little booklice
Try to improve their learning.

And if you creep up quietly
(Please don't disturb their classes)
You'll see that every booklouse needs
To wear a pair of glasses;

For reading strains such tiny eyes,
And little minds that feed
On books as big as skyscrapers,
Digesting all they read.

The Honey Bee Queen
Holds Court

The Honey Bee Queen
Holds court today,
Workers and drones
Dress-up and go
To hear just what
Their queen will say.

The hive is just buzzing,
Excitement is building;
All pollen is brushed
From cone, floor and ceiling;
Each cell is waxed
To smoothness and shine.

In the glow of sweet honey
Musicians are humming;
The jelly is royal
And served on a platter;
The hive is the home
Of bowing and scraping.

The Honey Bee Queen
Stands plump and tall,
Regal in black
And yellow and black;
Every bee hushes,
What will she say?
What will she say?

Patterning Patterning

butterfly wings
are fascinating
for each patterning
is repeated
butterfly wings
are fascinating
for each patterning
is repeated
butterfly wings
are fascinating
for each patterning
is repeated
butterfly wings
are fascinating
for each patterning
is repeated

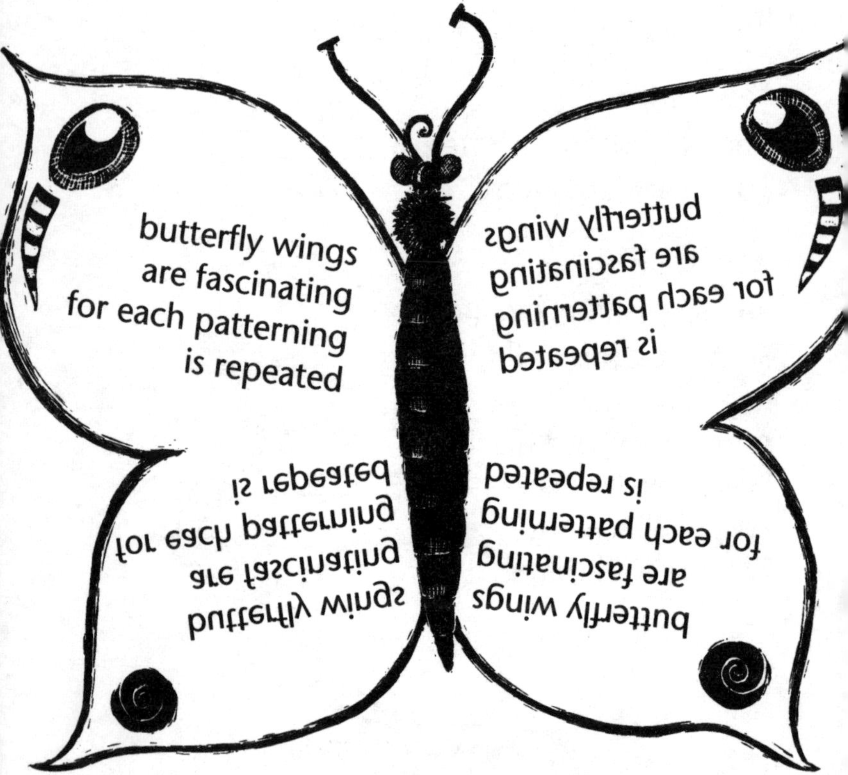

Beast

(A do-it-yourself poem)

I was walking through the jungle
When I stumbled on a beast
Who had teeth as sharp as _____,
He looked ready for a feast!
His coat was coarse like _____,
His eyes were mean and small,
His roar was like _____,
When he let out a call.
His muscles bulged like _____,
His back was broad and set,
So I chose not to disturb him
Or take him for a pet!

Sea Snake

Sea snake slipping through the water,
Black and white and black again;
Winding through the weeds of salt beds,
Hungry to inflict his pain.

Circling, seeking, wriggling by,
Silken movement, fixed-stare eye.
Deep fangs ready, small jaws part,
Paralysis of one small heart.

Red

(A tanka)

When we buried Red
the sunlight stroked his smooth coat
and gentled his bed,
because even in his death
the soft, petting day loved him.

Alligator

He's coming closer to the bank,
This animated, ruggéd plank;
He's climbing up with log-like lumber
And settling down into a slumber.
Without trust, his cold eyes wake,
Proving that his sleep was fake;
Ready and willing for a killing,
Hungry for a belly-filling.

Rule of Migration

A locust hopped into a restaurant,
Looked at the menu and said,
"Is this list of food just for starters?
Your customers are underfed!

"I'll start with some pies – make it sixty,
I'll swallow them down, all in pairs;
And when I have worked through your menu
I'll start on the tables and chairs.

"I've worked up an appetite travelling,
And I've learnt when I stop, without doubt,
That, although not akin to the creatures,
A locust must simply pig-out!"

The Rhythm of Death

Deep in the jungle the drums fill the air,
Monkeys and elephants travel with care,
Zebras and buffalo keep a look out
'Cause the rhythm in the air says that man is
about.

Why Barnacles Cling to Boats

(A tongue twister)

Boats bob about, banging their bottoms on
  barnacles,
And barnacles bang the bottoms of boats
  bobbing about –
So, sometimes barnacles cling to a boat's
  bobbing bottom,
And the banging boat bottom becomes a
  bobbing barnacle base!

TEACHERS
(And other school problems)

Lost Property

The Headteacher's announcement

"Hmm, hmm...

A sandwich has been spotted
In the corner of the hall,
Some say it has the odour
To anaesthetize us all;
It has crawled behind the benches,
Adding fluff balls to its grime,
And rolled under the wall-bars –
Must have been there for some time.

Miss Pope says, though she's not certain,
That she's seen it twice before;
Once sliding in the gym, then squashed
Underneath the library door.
And about a month ago, I've heard,
Mr Scott, our new caretaker,
Complained of mouldy, doughy smells
From behind a radiator.

If this over-active, agéd lunch,
Well-past its sell-by date,
Belongs to you then please act now
Before it is too late.
Lost property just cannot cope
With items that are squidgy,
Might I suggest unwanted food
Be returned home to your fridgy.

Hmm, hmm... Thank you."

Miss Eva Garibaldi

(A cautionary tale)

Miss Eva Garibaldi
Was a teacher of some years,
Whose career was punctuated
By her breaking down in tears.
The children rarely listened
To the lessons she'd prepared,
But chose to play a game or two,
Usually in pairs.

Miss Eva Garibaldi
Was a 'Miss', make no mistake,
She lived alone in Eastbourne,
Where she would very rarely break
The habits of her solitude,
Meticulously planned,
And where she played the tuba
In the local big brass band.

Miss Eva Garibaldi
Had patiently restrained
Her hand from making contact
With a bottom, and she'd tamed
A volatile volcano of
A temper that once drowned
The foghorn from the cliff top
Of her dearly loved home town.

Miss Eva Garibaldi
Was misjudged as weak and shy,
The tears she'd wept had hidden
Building anger in her eyes,
The children hadn't noticed
Curious changes in her mood,
And saw no reason to hold back
From being cruel and rude.

Miss Eva Garibaldi
Took the children on a trip,
(The sort you have to write about
When you've returned from it)
She took them to a cliff top
So they could admire the view,
Then she lifted up her tuba
And blew and blew and blew.

Miss Eva Garibaldi
Watched the children jump in fear
Of the strange and piercing noises
That played havoc with their ears.
Then Miss Eva Garibaldi
Went to the head to say
That her recent fear of teaching
Had been completely swept away.

So if you call a teacher names
Or show some disrespect,
Remember their reaction
Might not be what you expect.
She may dissolve in floods of tears
And abandon work that's planned,
But she might just take you on a trip
With a tuba in her hand.

Parrot Fashion

(A limerick)

There was a school teacher from York,
Who taught her young parrot to talk;
He recited his tables
And all Aesop's fables,
And then took a bow, with a squawk.

4×4=16

2×2=4

There's a Frog Down the Back of the Toilet, Miss

PUPIL:

There's a frog down the back of the
   toilet, Miss,
It's lodged itself under the pipe,
And I need to go sort of desperate, Miss,
Do you think it is likely to bite?

TEACHER:

The caretaker knows of the problem,
He's got it in hand, never fear;
Just go to the toilet, and quickly,
Now don't hold the lesson up, dear!

PUPIL:

> There's a spider on the lamp shade
>   above, Miss,
> And it stares when you sit on the seat,
> And I'm kind of scared it might fall,
>   Miss,
> And I don't mean on to my feet!

TEACHER:

> I'm sure there is no need to worry,
> Spiders are harmless and small,
> I think an attack is unlikely,
> Go now, child, or don't go at all! ☛

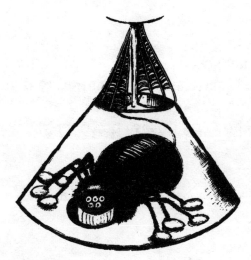

PUPIL:

> But there's a wasp flying round the
>   cistern, Miss,
> It's buzzing about to and fro,
> And I'd sort of feel quite exposed, Miss,
> Just sitting in wait down below.

TEACHER:

> I have no more time for your stories,
> But I see that you've started to dance
> From one leg on to the other,
> So go now, this is your last chance!

HALF AN HOUR LATER

TEACHER:

> What took you so long in the toilet,
>   child?
> You've missed half an hour of science
> Your excuse had better convince me
> Or I'll punish your blatant defiance!

PUPIL:

> Well, while I sat on the toilet, Miss,
> The wasp got caught in the web
> The spider had spun just above, Miss,
> It was almost touching my head! ☞

41

So I grabbed up my trousers quite
   smartish, Miss,
And got ready to leave pretty quick,
When I noticed my trousers were
   croaking, Miss,
And I started to feel sort of sick.

And as I stood still in the corner, Miss,
My trousers were leaping about,
And I was too frightened to move, Miss,
Too frightened even to shout!

Then out of the top of my trousers, Miss,
A little frog struggled and jumped
Up to the spider and wasp, Miss,
He swallowed them both in one lump.

Then SPLASH! the frog landed in water,
    Miss,
He swam around having great fun,
With legs hanging out of his mouth,
    Miss,
It was just like 'Wildlife on One'!

Then I flushed him away down the loo,
   Miss,
He swam with the flow, without pain,
I expect he'll escape very quickly, Miss,
When he comes to the end of the drain.

TEACHER:
   Your tale is less than convincing,
   You'll stay in at lunch for a week;
   And unless you can tell me the truth,
      dear,
   Please just don't bother to speak!

ENTER CARETAKER

CARETAKER:
   The boys' toilets are out of order,
   I hope no one's playing a joke,
   There's some kind of blockage to sort
      out,
   A blockage that happens to croak!

Flip-side Friend

She's always been my best friend,
My put it to the test friend,
More loyal than the rest friend
For years and years.

But now she is my worst friend,
My wants to see me cursed friend,
My hurts me 'til I burst friend
Into tears, into tears.

Stink

Up in the staffroom,
In the corner by the sink,
Is a strong, tall cupboard
That emits an awful stink.

There is a rumour spreading,
And I think it might be true,
That the cupboard holds a monster
Whose job it is to chew

On any naughty girl
Or any naughty boy
Daft enough to flout the rules,
Be late or just annoy

Mr Clegg, the headteacher,
Who has the only key, I think,
To the strong, tall cupboard
That emits an awful stink.

Sticks and Stones

I want to go back home right now,
Where everything's the same;
Where the chairs are warm and safe
And nobody wins games.
I want to curl up in a ball
And make the hours pass;
I want to disappear from sight,
Or run away from class.
I want to stop the tears coming,
I don't want my eyes red;
I want my mum to pick me up
And tuck me into bed.
They say that I'm too sensitive,
Perhaps I would agree,
But whilst sticks and stones might break
    my bones,
It's names that really hurt me.

Parents' Evening

Parents' evening, parents' evening,
Brings an end to all deceiving,
Parents' evening, parents' evening,
Brings an end to all deceiving.

Parents' evening's coming,
The world is looking black,
My parents think that I've tried hard,
I'd better go and pack.
I tried to hide the letter
But they found it in my bag,
They'll ground me for a month or two,
Isn't life a drag?

Parents' evening, parents' evening,
Brings an end to all deceiving,
Parents' evening, parents' evening,
Brings an end to all deceiving.

Parents' evening's coming,
My survival chance is slim,
I told them I get house points
But the teachers keep me in
For being rude and cheeky,
And for talking at the back,
For occasionally nicking
The odd thing that I lack.

Parents' evening, parents' evening,
Brings an end to all deceiving,
Parents' evening, parents' evening,
Brings an end to all deceiving.   ☞

Parents' evening's coming
So I've tried to make amends,
I've apologized to teachers
And treated them like friends.
I've requested the forgiveness
Of those who are so wise,
And asked if they could see their way
To telling a few lies.

Parents' evening, parents' evening,
Brings an end to all deceiving,
Parents' evening, parents' evening,
Brings an end to all deceiving.

Parents' evening's coming
And there's nothing I can do
To change my reputation
In just a day or two.
They'll say they're disappointed,
They expected more of me,
And I'll say that I've been a fool
Not to plainly see that...

Parents' evening, parents' evening,
Brings an end to all deceiving,
Parents' evening, parents' evening,
Brings an end to all deceiving.

With Reference to a Walk

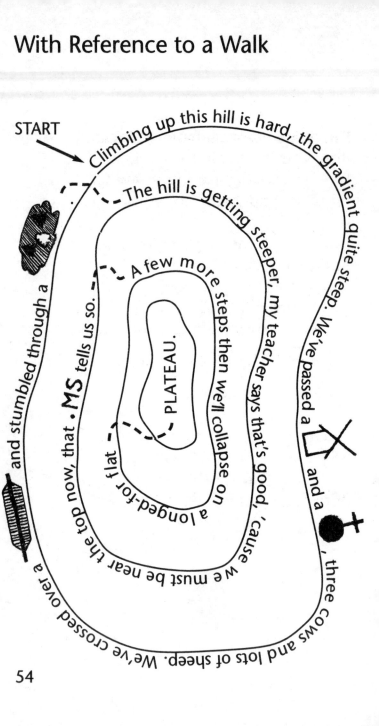

START

Climbing up this hill is hard, the gradient quite steep. We've passed a and a , three cows and lots of sheep. We've crossed over a and stumbled through a that. MS tells us so. A few more steps then we'll collapse on a longed-for flat PLATEAU. we must be near the top now, The hill is getting steeper, my teacher says that's good, 'cause

This poem relies on these symbols:

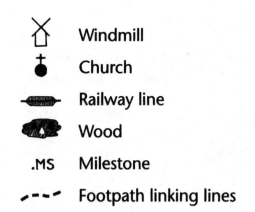

Windmill

Church

Railway line

Wood

.MS   Milestone

Footpath linking lines

The A Team

They're giving out in assembly today
The names of all the boys picked to play
In the A team.

It's bound to be Tom and Alex and Lee,
And I've heard Matt is being moved from
   the B
To the A team.

The whole school will sit in silence to hear
The list of boys that we will all cheer
In the A team.

And the rest of us boys will straighten our
    lips,
Fight back the tears and shout hip, hip, hips
For the A team.

Playing with Fire

Never cross our caretaker,
Never make him mad,
Never call him names
Or tell him that he's sad;
Never steal his tools,
Never nick his screws,
Never spike his coffee
While he's listening to the news;
Never laugh at his overalls
Even though they're baggy,
Never tell him that his tummy's
Getting rather saggy;
Never stay in the cloakroom
When he's trying to sweep,
Never make loud noises
When he's just gone off to sleep;
Never stuff your litter
Underneath his cupboard door,
Never drop your chewing gum
Upon his polished floor;
Never write your name upon
A desk with pen or pencil,
Never decorate his bucket,
Even with a stencil;

Never complain loudly
When his radio starts to boom,
'Cause he'll feed you to the dragon
He keeps in the boiler room!

'Big Boys' Don't Cry

'Big boys' do cry –
When nobody's looking
Or the teacher's back is turned;
In the corner of the park,
When they get home,
(Under the duvet cover).

'Big boys' do cry
Because words that sting
Can be flung so hard
That they can target
A 'big boy's' heart,
And stab out the tears.

Subtraction

Our French teacher keeps snails,
But we get quite suspicious
When she tells us that keeping snails
Is simply "So delicious"!

She also keeps pet frogs,
She says they're good for kissing,
But what we really want to know
Is why their legs are missing!

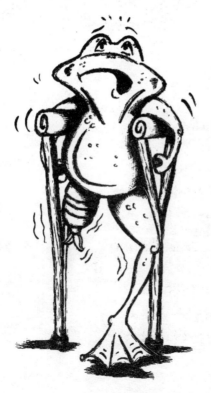

Changing Partners

Singing softly
Singing loudly
Counting in
And counting out,
Jumping, hopping,
Tripping, stopping,
Spinning like
A roundabout.
Skipping over
Skipping under
See the rope
Spin round and round,

Slipping under
Slipping over
Bottom slaps
The tarmac ground.
"You're out!"
"You're out!"
"See if I care,
Game was stupid anyway!"
"Break friends, break friends
Never ever make friends"
Changing partners
Every day.

The Game

Brian Collins knows the game,
He never has to suffer shame
Of sums marked X,
Of words crossed out;
Brian's got it all worked out.

Brian Collins knows the game,
He never drives Miss insane
With silly talk
And clumsy hands,
And all his work is carefully planned.

Brian Collins knows the game,
When it comes to charm, he's been trained.
His smile is wide,
His mind is keen,
And I bet he'll make the football team.

Brian Collins knows the game,
Miss never says that he's a strain.
Why is he him?
Why am I me?
Why were we made so differently?

You're Dead

If you copy from a friend
You're dead,
If you give the truth a bend
You're dead,
If you run instead of walk
Or shout instead of talk
You're dead,
You're dead;

If you forget your pencil case
You're dead,
If you make a funny face
You're dead,
If your pages are all blotchy
Your teacher will go potty
You're dead,
You're dead;

If you walk over the grass
You're dead,
If you pick your nose in class
You're dead,
If your reading book gets lost
You'll have to pay the cost
You're dead,
You're dead;

If you're talking at the back
You're dead,
If your fingernails are black
You're dead,
If you're late in your arriving
Not much chance of your surviving
You're dead,
You're dead;

If you fail the tables test
You're dead,
If you take a little rest
You're dead,
If your games kit's being washed
Or your topic's sort of squashed
You're dead,
You're dead;

If you jump the dinner queue
You're dead,
If your name's scratched on the loo
You're dead,
If your homework is in late
Then you'll have to meet your fate
You're dead,
You're dead;

If you're sent to see the head
You're dead,
If his face goes kind of red
You're dead,
If he reaches for the phone
And makes contact with your home...
YOU'RE DEAD.

69

FAMILY FEATURES
(Warts and all)

Objection

Aunty Rita calls me "pet",
It gets me in a rage;
I've never eaten 'Whiskers'
And I don't live in a cage!

MEOW!!

My Brother Likes to Windsurf

My brother likes to windsurf,
He thinks he's very good;
My sister says that he shows off
To the girls, and so he should!

If I was as big as my brother
I'd windsurf round the bay
And show off all my muscles,
And all the girls would say,

"Who is that hunk in trunks,
Windsurfing with such power?"
And they'd follow me back to the jetty
And talk to me for hours.

And I'd tell them about my yacht
That I'd left back at my mansion,
And about the fleet of aeroplanes
I'd bought from Richard Branson.

I'd tell them about the cups I'd won,
For football and for tennis,
And tell them how the publicity
Had come to be a menace.

I'd mention my world travel,
All the places that I'd been to,
The presidents and queens I'd met,
The stars and all the film crews.

And then I'd tell them how, one day,
When the planet was in danger,
I'd put my cape and mask on
And had been a hero stranger.

My brother likes to windsurf,
He's good, there is no question,
But when it comes to showing off
I could give him a lesson!

Wait a Minute

Wait a minute,
Wait a minute,
I'm busy now,
Just wait.

Wait a minute,
Wait a minute,
Not right now,
We're late.

In a while,
After lunch,
Will tomorrow do?
In the morning
Or next week,
In a month or two.
If I can,
When I can,
When the money's there.
Just be patient,
Don't be rude,
And don't say, "It's not fair!"

Wait a minute,
Wait a minute,
You're driving me
Quite mad.

Wait a minute,
Wait a minute,
Go and ask
Your Dad!

Man or Mouse?

Up in the attic,
At the corner of our house,
Lives our rather agéd uncle
Who believes he is a mouse!

He never causes trouble
When he squeezes through the gaps
From the attic to the kitchen,
Dodging all the traps.

When the cheese goes missing
No one says a word,
And the scurrying above us
We pretend we haven't heard.

Our neighbour once suggested
That we have a problem pest,
But, apart from his self-image,
We think Uncle is the best!

Vegetable Attack

When you ask Mum what's for dinner
And she goes sort of quiet,
Then gives you a long lecture on
What makes a healthy diet,
You know for sure what's coming
And thank God for your last snack,
Then brace yourself in ready for
A vegetable attack.

She lines up all her weapons,
Now strategically enrolled
To purge and purify the body,
Ousting gluttony from the soul.
She's ready to do battle
Underneath your spotty skin,
Committed fully to the cause
Of cleansing deep within.

Her cauliflower power bombs
Are camouflaged by cheese.
Her veggie soup with extra leeks
Can bring you to your knees.
Some days the fight is fought with speed,
She quickly gets the edge,
By throwing, without warning,
A grenade of stewed mixed veg.

On days of quiet espionage,
When you lie fearfully in wait
For the poisonous gas of Brussels sprouts
To engulf you from your plate,
It seems that she's retreated
So you burst into a ballad,
Until you open up the fridge
And get ambushed by a salad.

She says she does it out of love
And it's simply a health matter;
She claims that burgers, chips and cake
Will only make you fatter.
But when you smell the cabbage leaves
On her ammunition rack,
You doubt a love that can command
A vegetable attack.

My Aunt

Tight squeezer
Lipstick smudger
Story teller
Plant lover
Fast knitter
Baby sitter
Bus rider
Soap watcher
Tea drinker
Tea dancer
Old swinger
Day tripper
Letter writer
Kind thinker
Treat bringer
Real spoiler.

Smiling Through

My grandma's hobby
Is getting things 'done'
Cosmetic surgery –
Nose, bust and tum.

They've sucked out the fat,
And tucked in the skin,
And given my grandma
A permanent grin!

When my Dad Watches the News

When my dad watches the news…
You can start lots of fights
And swing from the lights,
You can throw all the cushions about,
You can smash every plate,
Keep on slamming the gate
And wear all your clothes inside out;
Do a dangerous trick
Or make yourself sick
By eating four packets of jelly,
You can 'prune' a few plants,
Donated by aunts,
Or draw Superman on his belly;
You can dig up the garden
Burp, and not say pardon,
Or write on the wall with a pen,
You can shout, "There's a fire!"
Or, "Mum's joined a choir!"
Or, "I'm leaving school when I'm ten!"
You can dance on the table,
For as long as you're able,
Then dive off the edge with *real* 'flare',
You can hair-gel the cat
So she's painful to pat,
You can staple your gran to the chair;

Phone a friend, in New York,
And have a long talk,
Or tell him, "You've won a world cruise."
You can juggle with eggs
Or shave the dog's legs,
When my dad watches the news.

Revenge

My brother chased me with a crab,
He found it by a rock,
But I WILL get my own back –
It's now inside his sock!

A Matching Pair

My aunty lives in a sea-shell,
At least that's what she told me,
But she can't really live in a sea-shell
She measures a full six foot three!

My uncle says he's a fairy,
Mum says that it's very sad,
'Cause his armpits are terribly hairy
And his breath smells incredibly bad.

Dad says they're made for each other,
Though their antics make others gape,
They're happy to live with each other
We're happy to make our escape!

Reasonable Parents

Some nights I hear my parents come into
 my room,
And I poke my book under the pillow,
And pretend to be asleep.
And that's when it happens...
They forgive me everything!

Mum says,
"He didn't mean to be so rude,
He just forgot himself;
And I think he's tried to tidy his room –
Well, at least his large bookshelf.
And it is quite hard to remember to say
'Thank you' all of the time,
In fact, I think he does very well,
We forget he's only nine!"

Then Dad says,
"I know he should have asked before
He took my tools from the shed,
But kids forget things like that
When they've got an idea in their head.
And it must be hard to go to bed
When you don't feel tired at all;
I remember reading under the covers –
A monkey, I was, I recall!"

And when I hear my parents go out of my
    room
I slide my book out from under the pillow,
Snuggle down, all safe,
And thank God for giving me such
    reasonable parents!

Little Lies

One day I told a little lie
That grew and grew and grew;
It filled my bedroom and the loft,
The bathroom and the loo.
It squashed itself into the lounge
The kitchen and the hall;
And then slid out under the door
And climbed the garden wall.

It covered gardens, houses, roads,
And then engulfed the city;
It sludged itself on hills and dales
And stopped them looking pretty.
And now I know that little lies
Grow big, just like Mum said;
Don't think I'll tell another one,
I'll try the truth instead.

Come Here!

(Mum's on the warpath!)

Beating, beating, my heart is beating,
Beating, beating, my heart is beating,
There is nothing worse
Than this sick, sick feeling
Beating, beating, my heart is beating,
I can see from her face
That it's not worth appealing.
Beating, beating, my heart is beating,
Thought I'd got away with it,
Thought I could just lie,
Beating, beating, my heart is beating,
I sort of knew that it was wrong
And now I know why,
Beating, beating, my heart is beating,
She's got the look, she's got the frown,
Any minute I'll be found,
Beating, beating, my heart is beating,
Her footsteps in the hallway
Make a threatening sound,
Beating, beating, my heart is beating,
The squeaking of the middle stair
Says she's getting near,
Beating, beating, my heart is beating,

I hear her sigh before she shouts
The dreaded words, "Come here!"
Beating, beating, my heart is beating,
Beating, beating, my heart is beating!
Beating, beating, my heart is beating!
Beating, beating, my heart is beating!

Sorry

Why is the word 'sorry'
So very hard to say?
Your mouth goes dry,
Your arms go stiff,
Your knees start to give way.
And even when that little word
Is ready to pop out,
It rolls around
Upon your tongue
Until you have to shout,
"I'M SORRY!", just to get it past
Your gums, your teeth, your lips;
And then your mum says,
"Well, my girl,
It doesn't sound like it!"

Noses

Nobody knows why noses grow to varying degrees, so I suppose nobody knows why one grew big on me!

My Sister Has Gone Loopy

My sister has gone loopy,
She smiles all of the time,
And when I lost her favourite tape
She simply said, "That's fine"!

I think she's got a temperature,
Her cheeks seem rather flushed;
Her eyes are glazed, she's in a daze,
Her brain has gone all mushed.

She says she loves the fluffy clouds,
She says she loves the trees,
But most surprisingly of all
She says that she loves me!

She said my Lego model
Had been, "very carefully planned",
She doesn't call me Titch or Pain,
I don't know where I stand.

Mum says just make the most of it,
She hasn't gone insane,
And when she's fallen OUT of love
She'll be herself again.

Grandad's Chair

Grandad always sits in a chair.
I've been told that, at one time, he did
    other things too;
But now Grandad always sits in a chair.
Some years ago he cycled fifteen miles
    a day;
Worked long and hard with his big,
    leathered hands;
Never felt a splinter, hardly felt a cut.

Grandad, I've been told, was a joker,
A twinkle in the eye sort of man,
He knew more jokes than the whole of
    my class,
And was a champion tickler.
Mum says Grandad used to:–
Cook the best chips you could ever taste;
Pull the funniest faces you could ever see;
Score the best goals you could ever score;
And tell the best stories you could ever hear.

Grandad fought in the Second World War.
He marched out with his brother
And marched back alone.
He stopped smiling for a while.

But now Grandad always sits in a chair
Because his legs won't do what his heart
    tells them.
Yet, when I've got a question or a problem,
I find the chair Grandad's sitting in
And ask him what I want to know,
And he's always got an answer!
When Grandad dies, his chair will be very
empty.

The Years Slip By

My grandma likes to ice-skate,
She's always at the rink,
She wears a shiny stretch-suit
In a sickly shade of pink.

She whizzes round quite quickly
And to increase her pace
She often takes her wig off,
Especially in a race.

Once when she was racing
Her opponent was much brisker,
So she jutted out her hairy chin
To win just by a whisker.

And when she plays ice-hockey,
If her team looks like it's losing,
She gums the opposition's legs,
Causing quite substantial bruising!

My grandad says he's never bored,
The time just seems to fly,
'Cause being married to my gran
Has made the years slip by.

Twice Removed

My Uncle Peter, twice removed,
Has a wart upon his nose,
It's grown enormous recently,
Why, nobody knows.
I know they say that if you lie
Your nose will get much longer,
But what a growing wart can mean
Has made me really ponder.
It used to be just like a pea
And then more like a sprout,
But now it's got to cabbage size,
I think, without a doubt,
My Uncle Peter, twice removed,
Should seek medical advice,
Show the wart to expert eyes
('Cause it isn't very nice!)
Then have the wart, at once, removed,
Just once, hear what I've said,
'Cause to have the wart twice removed
Might deprive him of his head!

A Very Rare Condition

(A ballad)

Jeremy Fast had two left feet,
The teachers all agreed,
He couldn't run, he couldn't jump,
And was often called a weed.

Mr Beat, the PE teacher,
Had very little time
For boys who couldn't kick a ball
Or run in a straight line.

One afternoon, out on the field,
When rain was crashing down,
Poor Jeremy was made to race
Himself into the ground.

And Beat just bellowed, red in face,
To make the lad go faster,
Then Fast fell down into the mud –
Plastered with disaster.

On sports days Jeremy would sigh
And mourn his lack of speed,
He knew at some point Beat would shout,
"Fast! You're last! You weed!"

And Emily, pride of Woodpark School,
With hair all blonde and sleek,
Would be heard to say she couldn't stand,
"Boys all thin and weak!"

"All boys should have big muscles,
Be athletic, fast and strong."
Poor Jeremy looked down at himself
And wondered what was wrong

With boys whose bodies didn't match up
To Schwarzenegger's figure,
Whose arms and legs had never lifted
Weights with any vigour.

One night, at home, just after tea,
Fast asked his dad a question
That made the man wince and complain
Of violent indigestion.

"You want to come down the gym?"
Mouthed his dad, in quite a sweat,
"Why don't you work out here, at home,
You're just not ready yet

To expose yourself to all the lads,"
(By that he meant his friends)
"Best build your body a little more,
While you've got time to spend."

107

So Jeremy took his dad's advice,
He exercised for weeks;
He lifted weights, he cycled bikes,
And flexed from head to feet.

Then after weeks of agony,
He entered for a race;
Announced to all his classmates that
They'd wonder at his pace.

And Emily, pride of Woodpark School,
With hair all blonde and sleek,
Said if he won he could carry her bag
To lessons for a week.

The race day came and Fast stripped off
To show his new physique,
But he still came last and heard Beat shout,
"No cure for two left feet!"

Then one day Fast didn't come to school,
And he was really missed,
Except by Beat, the PE teacher,
"Such a relief!" he hissed,

"I've pulled my hair out because of him,
And what's left has gone grey."
Then he danced around the changing rooms
Singing "What a lovely day!"

The very next day Mrs Fast sent a note
To say that Jeremy
Was at present in Woodpark hospital,
Ward six, bed number three,

And that friends were welcome to visit him if,
And then she made this addition,
They could promise that they wouldn't ask
About his very rare condition.

Well Smudge and Gaffer went along,
Taff, Swot and Nigel Tate –
Who'd never had a nickname,
Although he was a mate –

And Sharon Brown and Tracy Flynn,
Who did everything together,
And Sharon's little brother, Tim,
Whose hair stood up like feathers.

But Emily, pride of Woodpark School,
With hair all blonde and sleek,
Said she couldn't be seen to visit a boy
Who was so thin and weak.

The company stood around the bed,
Bed number three, ward six,
And offered Fast some goodies,
There was really quite a mix.

Swot's mum had sent him with some grapes,
Taff had brought a cake,
Gaffer had brought a magazine
(Three months out of date),

The girls had brought a whole bag of things,
Said they couldn't do enough,
And Smudge gave him two chocolate
    squares –
When he'd picked off the fluff!

Jeremy thanked his loyal friends
As they pulled up some chairs,
Then things went quiet, they looked at their
    feet,
And tried hard not to stare

At the metal frame over his legs,
Covered with a sheet,
They knew they mustn't mention it
And definitely not peep.

"So when d'ya think they'll let you home?"
Asked the girls, together,
"Probably at the end of next week,
It all depends on whether

115

"The operation has been a success,"
And then he made this addition,
"But let's not get morbid and talk about
My very rare condition."

The silence bounced from wall to wall,
Each sniff seemed like a shout;
The friends looked at each other
And then for the way out.

"We'd better be going." said Swot in a sweat,
"We don't want to tire you out!"
"You'll soon be back at school," smiled Taff,
"Of that there is no doubt."

They waved when they reached the sign
    'Exit',
And silently ended their mission,
All separately wondering about the frame
And Fast's very rare condition.

Some weeks later, with Sports Day
   approaching,
Fast strolled back through the gates,
He watched all the pupils in training
And shouted advice to his mates.

He asked Mr Beat if he could run on the day
As he'd been in training at home;
Beat said "Lad, you can run in each race
As long as you leave me alone!"

Then Smudge and Gaffer slapped Fast's back
In an encouraging sort of way,
And Taff and Swot and Nigel Tate
Let out, "Hip hip hooray

"For our friend Fast who doesn't give up
   Even after a hospital stay!"
And Sharon and Tracy smiled sugar and spice
In a duplicate sweet sort of way.

Sports Day came very quickly and Beat
Was putting them all through their paces,
He warmed them up and put them in groups,
And read out the order of races.

Fast's name was read out a number of times,
Causing Beat to stutter a lot,
Beat said, "You've five minutes to get on
   the field,
Just be there, r... r... ready or not!"

The changing rooms buzzed with excitement,
The children opened their lockers,
And trainers and shorts tumbled on to
   the floor.
(Some of the socks were real shockers!)

In less than five minutes the field was awash
With children of varying sizes,
All talking about which team would win
Most of the coveted prizes.

But Emily, pride of Woodpark School,
With hair all blonde and sleek,
Said she couldn't possibly run in a race
When she hadn't quite reached her peak. ☛

The tension was mounting, the chanting
    began,
Race number one had begun;
Taff was cheered for coming in third
But it was Jeremy Fast who won!

"Just a fluke!" said Beat to a colleague,
"Fast is no athlete at all;
In his next race he's bound to come last
Or not to finish after a fall."

But Fast went on to more glory,
And everyone watched, quite astounded,
As Fast led the field in all of his races
And left all his critics dumbfounded!

At the end of the day, when awards had
    been made
And Fast was walking away,
A hush filled the air as Beat shouted out,
"What got into you, lad, today?"

"Where have you trained? What have you
    eaten?
Who is your coach? Tell me now.
At one time you couldn't run a straight line
But now you're a champion! How?"

Jeremy smiled as he looked at the crowd,
A sea of inquisitive faces,
And then he bent down to his trainers
And slowly undid the laces.

He slipped his trainers from his feet
And then removed his socks;
The crowd gaped, stunned by what they saw,
It was a day for shocks!

"The scars," said Beat, "On your right foot,
Now tell us, what are those?"
"The scars," said Fast, "Are simply where
They rearranged my toes,

"So now I haven't got two left feet,
I've got a left and right,
And I've got you to thank, Mr Beat,
'Cause you made me aware of my plight." ☛

125

In silence the crowd dispersed and got
    changed
And then they all went home,
Apart from Fast who suddenly found
That he was quite alone

With Emily, pride of Woodpark School
With hair all blonde and sleek,
"You can carry my bag home if you want."
She said all mild and meek.

"Carry your bag?" said Fast with a grin,
As he gave his tie a tweak,
"No thanks, I can't be seen with a girl
Who hasn't quite reached her peak."

In Verse

A brand-new series of poetry guaranteed to challenge, inspire and intrigue...

Pictures in my mind
Joan Poulson

If you think poetry is about flowers and fairies – think again! Think of snails and bagels and space travel. Think of the way you feel about going to a new school or when someone you love dies. Think of problems with teachers or with your mum's new boyfriend. Whatever you think, Joan Poulson's poetry will make you think again!

For more information about **In Verse**, please contact: The Sales Department, Macdonald Young Books, 61 Western Road, Hove, East Sussex BN3 1JD